BUMPING INTO GOD

Jenny Dyer

'Bumping into God' was first broadcast on BBC Radio Merseyside.

Cartoons and front cover illustration by Philip Spence.

ISBN 1 85852 204 8

CONTENTS

A TOY STORY

Let me introduce you to Jessica. Jessica is a little girl who has a habit of bumping into God in the strangest of places. For instance, take last Wednesday at nursery school. Jessica was fed up, so she went in search of God and found him in the play-house, wedged into a tiny chair reading *Winnie-the-Pooh*.

'Why can't I play in the car?' said Jessica. 'Andrew's been in it for ages.'

'Why can't Andrew play in it for as long as he wants to?' God said from behind his book.

'Why can't he learn to share?' said Jessica. 'Why can't I have a turn?'

'Why can't you play with something else?' asked God.

'Why should I?' asked Jessica.

God sighed and closed his book in the manner of someone who sees he's going to get no peace. 'Now,' he said, 'do you ever see grown-ups squabbling over toys?'

'Do grown-ups have toys?' asked Jessica.

'Would you like a cup of tea?' asked God. God and Jessica hunted around on the floor, found themselves two little plastic cups and saucers and poured themselves two pretend cups of tea.

'Mum says she wishes she had more time to play with,' said Jessica. 'Does that mean time is a toy for her?'

'Ah!' said God. 'Is time a toy? Is independence a toy? Privacy? A certain standard of living?'

Jessica felt that the conversation was getting a bit above her.

'Is a toy just something you like to have and you don't want anyone else to take away?' she asked.

'Like a little peace and quiet to read?' suggested God.

'If grown-ups have toys too, what's the difference between grown-ups and children, 'sept size?' asked Jessica.

'What indeed?' said God, draining the last of his cup of tea.

'Are the only really grown-up people ones who think about what other people want, not what they want?' asked Jessica.

'Ah!' said God in a congratulatory sort of way. 'Would you like another cup of tea?'

GO TO YOUR ROOM

When Jessica stormed into her bedroom, God was there straightening her duvet.

'You been sent to your bedroom?' he asked.

'NO!' said Jessica.

'Mum cross with you, is she?' he asked.

'NO!' said Jessica.

'Want to talk about it?' asked God.

'NO!' said Jessica.

Perhaps to avoid further conversation, she pulled the duvet off the bed and began making a den with it over a chair. Several soft toys and Jessica went inside it and so did God, because he was told to.

'Now I'm going to take my children to the park,' announced Jessica, rounding up the soft toys and pushing them out. 'All except for teddy. He's been naughty so he's got to stay here with you as a punishment.'

'I'm not sure I like being cast in the role of ogre,' God objected mildly.

'Hello! We're back again!' said Jessica, pushing the soft toys back in. 'Has teddy behaved himself?'

'Oh yes,' said God. 'We're big pals, aren't we, teddy?'

'I'd just had him up to here,' explained Jessica in a very grown-up way.

'Children can be very trying,' agreed God.

'Do you ever get cross with your children?' asked Jessica.

'Unspeakably,' said God.

'Do you send them to their bedrooms?' asked Jessica.

'They take themselves off,' said God, 'and I spend my time trying to get them to come back. Speaking of which, isn't it time you and teddy made up?'

Jessica gave teddy a hug. 'What was that, teddy?' she said. 'Oh! Teddy says he's sorry he was naughty.'

'That's nice,' said God. 'Now, why don't you go downstairs and tell Mum you're sorry *you* were naughty?'

' 'Cos I'm not,' said Jessica.

'Well, go and give her a hug,' said God. 'Perhaps saying sorry can come later.'

BEDTIME PRAYERS

Jessica had been lying in bed brooding for some time, so she decided to trot along to the bathroom to break the boredom. In the bathroom she was surprised to find God doing a spot of cleaning.

'The lady in Sunday School says I should say prayers every night,' said Jessica. 'Why should I say prayers every night?'

'And what objection would you have,' asked God, 'to saying prayers every night?'

' 'Cos most of the time I don't feel like you're listening,' said Jessica.

'If your mum helps you to write 'Love from Jessica' on a birthday card and you put it in the postbox, how do you know that it gets there?' asked God.

'Mum doesn't pray,' said Jessica.

'Doesn't she?' asked God.

'When Mrs Andrews asked Mum to pray about her sister, Mum said she would, but she didn't,' said Jessica.

'How do you know that she didn't?' said God. 'How do you know that she wasn't praying while she was talking to Mrs Andrews, and while walking home, and when she phoned Mrs Andrews to ask how her sister was?'

'Does Mum pray every night, then?' asked Jessica.

'How should I know?' asked God and Jessica gave him one of her best scowls. 'Does it matter when and how she does it so long as it suits her and me?' God asked.

'So what's the point in me praying when I don't feel like it, like when I'm cross, and saying things I don't mean, like thank you for people I don't like,' asked Jessica.

'Can you think of a better way of learning to mean them?' asked God.

'But I just feel like I'm talking to myself and you're not listening,' said Jessica, thoroughly irritated.

God just carried on cleaning the mirror. 'There, that's much better,' he said, 'Can you see your face in it?'

'No, I can just see yours.'

'Oh? And why's that?'

' 'Cos I'm not in the right place to see my face, only to see yours, silly,' said Jessica.

'Ah!' said God, 'Perhaps praying is putting yourself in the right place to see me and not you. Now you get back to bed before your Mum realises you're on the loose.'

ALL DRESSED UP

Jessica went up to her bedroom to play with her dressing-up box, and found God was there tidying her wardrobe. He said he liked to make himself useful. Jessica put on her old bridesmaid's dress and paraded up and down. ''Course it's a bit small now,' she said. 'The zip won't do up.'

She took it off and put on the red jumper instead. 'This used to be Mum's,' she said, 'but it went all tight and funny in the washing machine so Mum gave it to me.' She put on her red fireman's hat as well and put out several fires in the corner of the bedroom.

'The hat's seen better days, too,' remarked God.

'Yes, it got left at the bottom of the garden,' said Jessica. 'Mum tried to throw it away but I got it out of the bin again 'cos it's my favourite.'

Now that all the fires were out, Jessica leant on the end of the bed and watched what God was doing. 'Do you ever dress up?' she asked.

'In a manner of speaking,' said God.

'What do you dress up as?'

'I put on people's insides, not their outsides,' said God.

Jessica was intrigued. 'What's people's insides like?'

'Ooh, they vary. Some make me feel lovely, some make me feel exciting, some make me feel sad.'

'Why do some make you feel sad?'

'Because some of them are all battered and broken like your fireman's hat.'

'Do you throw them away?'

'No, those tend to be my favourites. And then some of them are too small, like your bridesmaid's dress.'

'Like me?' asked Jessica.

'No, people's insides are different from their outsides. Little people like you are big on the inside. But sometimes as people grow up they get all small and tight inside because bad things happen to them.

'Like Mum's red jumper,?' asked Jessica.

'Yes, precisely like your Mum's red jumper,' said God.

'What then?' asked Jessica.

'I try to help them grow big again, if they'll let me,' said God.

'What if the threads go pop?' asked Jessica.

'You're stretching the analogy,' said God.

A TERRIBLE MESS

One afternoon Jessica and her Mum went to the park. Jessica's Mum sat on a bench to read her magazine while Jessica fed the ducks. Something was worrying Jessica, so after all the bread was gone she went to sit on a different bench and she wasn't surprised to find that the man reading a newspaper next to her was God.

'Look at all the mess,' said Jessica.

'Yes, it is a terrible mess, isn't it?' said God.

'You're not looking,' scolded Jessica. 'You're reading the newspaper.'

'I make it my business to keep abreast of world events,' said God.

'There's all sorts of nasty things in the lake that shouldn't be there,' Jessica pursued. 'There's a shopping trolley and plastic bags and bottles and sweet papers and cans and a milk crate and all sorts of dirty stuff. How did all that stuff get there?'

'Heaven knows,' conceded God.

'Can't you do something about it?' asked Jessica.

'Why should I?' asked God.

'You made everything didn't you?' said Jessica.

'Rumour has it,' said God.

'Well, can't you make it again, only better this time?' asked Jessica.

'I didn't make it to be like this,' said God.

'No, so can't you put it back like it's supposed to be?'

'Can't you?' suggested God.

'No, I can't', said Jessica. 'I'm only little and there's only one of me.'

'Oh, you'd be surprised,' said God, 'Two and two and fifty make a million, you know.'

But Jessica didn't understand because they don't do Maths at nursery school. 'And anyway,' she said, 'I didn't make all the mess.'

'Hm,' said God, 'they all say that.'

Jessica thought that sometimes God could be very horrible. 'It's you should do something, not me. I thought it's you who's supposed to be in charge,' she said.

God put down his newspaper and put a kind arm round her shoulders. Jessica was surprised to see that he was looking very, very serious.

'I thought so, too,' he said.

TEDDY BASHING

Jessica was in her bedroom beating the living daylights out of her teddy and muttering murderous threats when she discovered to her embarrassment that God was looking over her shoulder.

'What's teddy done to deserve this?' he asked.

'It's not teddy. It's my friend Charlotte,' said Jessica.

'Hm, even worse,' said God.

'She won't talk to me,' said Jessica. 'She says I broke her clown puppet but I didn't. And anyway, she wouldn't let me play with it.'

'Ah,' said God. 'Correct me if I'm wrong but didn't this incident take place several weeks ago?'

'Yes,' said Jessica.

'Dear, dear. Have you said to Charlotte that you're sorry about the puppet?'

'I'm not.'

'Well then, have you told her that you don't like not talking and asked her to be your friend again?'

'Yes,' said Jessica.

'And what did she say?' asked God.

'She just pulled a face and went off and giggled with her silly friends,' said Jessica, her eyes filling with tears.

'I see,' said God. He put an arm round Jessica's shoulders and helped her to blow her nose. 'Do you know what worries me about this?' he asked.

'What?' said Jessica.

'Well, it doesn't really matter whether Charlotte talks to you or not . . .'

'Yes, it does!' said Jessica.

'But all this teddy-bashing,' said God, 'does worry me. I don't like you getting all cross and spiteful inside and staying like that for weeks.'

Jessica disengaged herself from God's arm and turned to look at teddy. Teddy was still smiling but his smile looked a bit more fixed than usual, and his ear was starting to come unstitched.

'Do you think teddy needs a cuddle too?' asked God.

Jessica picked teddy up and cuddled him fit to burst. Teddy was all soft and nice. And, thanks to God, so was Jessica.

DOWN TO EARTH

A little while after Nan's funeral, Jessica went with her mother to sort out the flowers on Nan's grave. Jessica found it difficult to associate the mound of earth with her Nan so she wandered off by herself and found God planting bedding plants in a flower border.

'Ashes to ashes, dust to dust,' said God without looking up. 'Trust them to look on the miserable side. Now, you look at that.'

He held out to her a trowel full of earth. It just looked like soil to Jessica.

'Leaf mould,' God explained, 'dug it in last autumn. Life to life, that's what I say. Leaf to leaf. Flower to flower.'

'Is my Nan in heaven?' said Jessica.

'You don't sound very happy about that,' said God. 'Don't you want your Nan to be in heaven? My most marvellous creation?'

'What's heaven like?' asked Jessica.

God straightened his back. 'What,' he asked, 'do you think your Nan would like it to be like?'

'Does she have to wear a long white dress-thing?' asked Jessica.

'Heaven preserve us!' remarked God. 'Do you really think your Nan would be seen dead in a white nightie and wings, sitting on a cloud playing a harp?' God began cleaning his glasses with his hanky, apparently unaware that he was covering both of them with soil.

'I think,' said Jessica, and her lip quivered, 'my Nan would like to be where I am. She always said I was her most favouritest person of all.' Two big tears rolled down her cheeks.

'Then how could you imagine that she will ever leave you?' said God.

God put his glasses back on, pulled a face and took them back off again. He crouched down in front of Jessica and gave her a very kind look.

'Don't you worry about your Nan,' he said, and just for once he sounded deadly serious. 'I know what I'm doing.'

MISSING PRESUMED ABSENT

When Jessica first started at the big school, the infants' school, she found it very difficult. Her uniform felt so odd, all the children seemed so big and the teacher didn't smile. Jessica had rather got into the habit of bumping into God whenever she felt a bit low, so she was surprised not to see him around anywhere on the first day. She didn't see him on the second day either. On the third day she went looking for him. At break she spent so long looking for him amongst the coat-pegs that the teacher told her off. Then she saw a man gardening at the front of the school and she was sure it must be him. But when she ran up to him, it wasn't.

On the fourth day, Jessica had given up looking for God and spent the breaks standing watery-eyed at the edge of the playground. Then during the afternoon break she noticed a girl in a pink coat standing on her own, all tearful just like her. Jessica went up to her, took her hand, and said, 'Why are you crying?'

'I don't like school,' said the girl in the pink coat.

'I don't either,' said Jessica. 'Will you be my friend?'

After that, Jessica just knew she'd find God somewhere. And sure enough there he was in her bedroom when she got home from school.

'Where've you been?' she said.

'I've been around,' said God.

'Well, I looked everywhere for you!' said Jessica.

'On the contrary,' said God, 'you looked everywhere except where I was. It frequently seemed to me that you were *trying* not to find me.'

'Well I wasn't,' said Jessica. 'I needed you.' She sat on the bed next to God and he put his arm round her.

'I know,' he said. 'Don't worry about it. It happens like that sometimes.'

'I wanted to talk to you,' said Jessica.

'Well, I was watching you all the time,' said God, 'and you finally found me when you thought about someone else. Remember that if it happens again.'

ARTIST AT WORK

Jessica was painting a picture when she noticed God sitting at her elbow. 'What are you doing here?' she said.

'Oh, I like to watch a fellow artist at work,' said God.

'Do you do painting, then?' asked Jessica.

'Painting, modelling, anything creative,' said God.

'What sort of things do you make?' asked Jessica.

'This and that. Most things really. Well, everything actually,' said God modestly, but Jessica wasn't listening.

'This is going to be a picture of next door's cat,' she said.

'Ah yes, I was just going to ask,' said God.

'Only it doesn't sort of look right,' said Jessica.

'Ah,' said God. 'Sometimes things have a will of their own and don't turn out at all as you intend. That's one of the worst and best things about being an artist. Hey, what are you doing now?'

'It didn't work so I'm going to scrumple it up and put it in the bin,' said Jessica.

'Oh no no no, you must never do that. The skill of the artist is to see the possibilities in an otherwise unpromising piece of work and transform it into something really special.'

Jessica sighed and picked up her brush again. 'There now, that looks better,' said God. 'Er . . . what is it?'

'It's a forest now,' said Jessica. 'You see, that's a tree and that's a bird and that's a tree that's been cut down.

'Ah, yes. Now that you've explained it, I can see it. Sometimes we have to see things through the eyes of the artist before we can discern their true meaning.'

'Yes,' said Jessica.

'Is that picture for me?' asked God.

'No,' said Jessica. 'I made it so I'm going to keep it. I'm not giving it away to anyone.'

'Ah yes,' said God. 'I know exactly what you mean.'

FORGIVE AND FORGET

When Jessica got home from school, God was in her bedroom sorting out her toys.

'I suppose you've come because you're cross,' said Jessica, throwing her satchel on the floor.

'No,' said God.

'You're cross 'cos I pulled Emma's hair,' said Jessica. She sat on the edge of her bed, arms folded, in a huff. 'But I don't want to talk about it.'

'Fair enough,' said God.

'It was her fault, anyway, 'cos she pinched me first,' said Jessica.

'Well, it doesn't matter now,' said God, soothingly.

'And the teacher made us both stand by the radiator but then she said afterwards we could join in again.'

'Well, it's all in the past then, isn't it?' said God. 'All over and dealt with.'

'And Emma and me said we were sorry. And Emma said she'd be my friend again and I said I'd be hers,' said Jessica.

'Well, there you are then,' said God.

'So there's no need to still be cross,' said Jessica, kicking the leg of the bed.

'I'm not,' said God. 'Forgive and forget, that's my motto.'

'Were you very cross?' asked Jessica.

'Umm . . . I was a bit at the time,' God admitted, 'but not now. There's no sense in staying cross for long.'

'No, 'cos it wasn't a very important thing, really,' said Jessica.

'No indeed,' said God.

'And lots of other people do much worse things only the teacher doesn't see,' said Jessica.

'I imagine you're right,' said God.

'So can we talk about something else instead?' asked Jessica.

'Why not?' said God. 'That would suit me fine.'

' 'Cos it really, really wasn't me who started it,' said Jessica.

'Jessica!' said God.

'Oh, sorry,' said Jessica.

WINTER CHILLS

It was the first really frosty day and Jessica was outside in her coat and wellies, with her hands in her pockets and wishing she had gloves on really. She found that God was outside too, chopping down some dead Michaelmas Daisy stalks.

'Why does it have to get cold and all the leaves and flowers die?' asked Jessica. 'I like the paddling pool and going to the beach and playing out after tea.'

'But do you think you'd enjoy all that so much if you could do it all year round?' asked God.

'Yes!' said Jessica.

'Well then,' said God, 'what about Christmas? If there wasn't winter there wouldn't be any Christmas, would there?'

Jessica sniffed and wiped her nose on her sleeve. 'Why not?' she said. 'Mum's auntie has Christmas in the summer in Australia.'

'Ah,' said God. He straightened up and examined his shears in a thoughtful sort of a way. 'To everything there is a season,' he said, 'a time to be born and a time to die, a time to plant and a time to pluck, a time to mourn and a time to dance.'

Jessica sniffed again. 'Well, I think it would be better if it was summer all the time and people didn't have to be unhappy and die and all that,' she said.

'Well,' said God, somewhat abashed, 'do you think it would be a good kind of world with everyone living for ever and everything always being the same?'

'Yes,' said Jessica, 'it would be better.'

God picked a dead poppy stalk with a fat seed head and twirled it in a thoughtful sort of way. 'How do you explain to a pupa the need for the chrysalis or describe to it a butterfly?' he said. Jessica wiped her nose on her sleeve again. 'One day you will understand,' said God.

'That's not fair!' said Jessica. 'Everybody says I'm too young to understand things.' God slipped the poppy stalk into Jessica's duffle-coat buttonhole. Seeds fell out as he did so. 'When will I be old enough, then?' she asked.

'When the seeds have grown,' said God.

BELIEVING AIN'T EASY

Jessica was dawdling home from school twenty yards behind her Mum when God caught up with her and fell into step.

'Hallo,' he said.

'My friend Charlotte says she doesn't believe in you,' said Jessica. 'Her Mum says you only exist in stories, like fairies and witches.'

God looked slightly bewildered. 'Tell me,' he said, 'Does Charlotte believe in Father Christmas?'

'Yes, of course,' said Jessica.

'Curious,' said God.

'Why shouldn't she believe in Father Christmas?' asked Jessica. God muttered something incomprehensible about different levels of reality. Jessica tried again:

'Charlotte says she looks and looks but she doesn't ever see no daft old man tidying her bedroom or digging no garden,' she said.

God considered. 'See that woman across the road?' he said. 'Tell me about her.'

'She's very, very old,' said Jessica, 'but she's nice and she always smiles at me and Mum when I'm going to school or coming home.'

'Good,' said God. 'Now, another person might have said, as bad a case of osteoporosis as I've seen in a long time. Another might say, a woman in frightful boots and a coat fit only for a jumble sale. Another might say, that's my Grandma. See?'

'What's that supposed to mean?' said Jessica.

'That you look, but what you see depends as much on what's inside you as what you're looking at,' said God.

'Oh,' said Jessica. 'How can I put the right things inside Charlotte, then?'

But God seemed lost in thoughts of his own. 'You still think I'm real, don't you?' he asked.

'Oh yes,' said Jessica soothingly. 'I told Charlotte I can mostly always find you if I want you, and sometimes you're there if I don't want you too, worse luck, and sometimes you say nice comfortable things and sometimes you say really strange things and I reckon if you can do all that you must be real.'

'Ah,' said God, 'out of the mouths of babes and infants.'

A COMFY LAP

Jessica had had a rotten day. The night before she'd been playing in her bedroom for far too long after Mum had told her to put the light out and she had been far too fast asleep this morning to get up for school. She'd mucked around with her breakfast for so long that they were late getting to school. Then she had got told off by the teacher for talking. One of the boys had pulled out her hair ribbon and the teacher had put it back in all wrong. And on the way home she had stepped in a puddle and got water in her shoes and Mum was livid.

When Jessica got home she was all watery-eyed and wished she'd never got up at all. She was about to go and see if God was in her bedroom when she realised that he was in the lounge watching the telly and drinking a mug of tea. She sniffed. 'Aren't you supposed to be doing something useful?'

'I'm being available,' he said.

Jessica hurled her coat into a corner and sat on the floor with a bump to take her shoes off.

'Want to tell me all about it?' asked God, putting the mug down where it wouldn't get knocked over.

'No,' said Jessica, feeling somewhat better already if the truth be told.

She scrambled up onto God's lap and curled up, sucking the end of her hair, like Mum would never let her. God stroked her head gently and together they watched the children's programmes. God was nice, thought Jessica. He had a nice way of being around when you needed him. He had a nice way of talking, not like most grown-ups. And being curled up in his lap was the best and nicest and safest place in the whole world.

ANYTHING

Jessica was giving her doll a bath in the washing-up bowl and God had been appointed to hold the towel.

'I have to be very careful not to get water in her open and shut eyes,' said Jessica.

'Quite so,' said God.

Jessica lifted the dripping doll from the bubbles, laid her on the towel on God's lap, wrapped her up and cuddled her.

'She's only a very tiny baby so I have to keep her warm,' she said.

'You'll make a wonderful mother,' said God.

Jessica laid the wrapped doll on the end of a long line of toys against the kitchen cupboard. 'Uh oh,' she said, 'Charles the Tiger's missing. He's always running off.'

Charles the Tiger was found to be on the floor outside the kitchen door. 'There, now I've got all my children together at last,' said Jessica.

'Like a cup of coffee?' said God, finding two toy cups. 'You must be worn out.'

'Oh, I am,' said Jessica, taking the proffered cup with a sigh and a mop of the brow that were clearly drawn from life. 'I have so many children . . .'

'. . . that you don't know what to do,' said God. 'I know the feeling.'

'They're always crying or needing feeding and changing and things. I never get a moment to myself,' said Jessica, wiping a doll's face and straightening an elephant's trunk. God was entertained.

'No,' he said, 'parenthood can be very demanding.'

'And they're always being so naughty,' said Jessica. 'Oh no, Charles is trying to run off again!'

'Yes, terrible, isn't it?' said God. 'Why do we carry on? Perhaps we should just throw them all out of the window.'

'Oh no,' said Jessica. 'They're my babies and I love them all.'

'Yes, of course you do,' said God.

'And I'd do anything for them,' said Jessica.

'Yes, of course you would,' said God.

BEING THERE

Jessica was sitting on her bed, crying, when she realised that God was sitting at her elbow. Suddenly overwhelmed by a desire to hit out, she turned to him and beat her fists on his chest. God let her finish, and then quietly put an arm round her.

'My friend Kate's in hospital again,' said Jessica between huge sobs. 'She's always in hospital.' She had to wait for the sobs to subside a bit, then she said: 'Why don't you make her better, like Jesus did to lots of people? Aren't you as clever as Jesus?'

God had the sense not to comment, and they sat like that for a long time.

'Will you promise me something?' said Jessica.

'What?' said God.

'Will you be there tonight if she gets frightened and needs to talk to someone?' said Jessica.

'Of course,' said God.

'Will you be there when she has her operation?' asked Jessica.

'Of course,' said God.

A worrying thought struck Jessica. 'Will they let you in?' she asked.

'To the operating theatre?' said God. 'Of course,' he said. 'They can't keep me away.'

'That's alright,' said Jessica, snuggling up to his sleeve. She wasn't quite sure that it was alright, but she needed to feel better.

'Why do people have to be ill?' Jessica asked. God squeezed her close.

'Why don't you always make people better?' asked Jessica. 'Don't you care enough?' God squeezed her close but said nothing.

A sudden thought struck Jessica again, and she looked round at God. 'If Jesus could always make people better, why did he die?' she asked. She met God's eyes, and saw that he looked very very sad, and very gentle. She had a strange feeling like looking into a deep well. It wasn't frightening though, and made her want to go on looking.

'You *do* care about Kate, don't you,' she said at last.

'More than you could know,' said God.